Sleeping Beauty

Coloring & Craft Book

Written and Illustrated by Vanessa Salgado

ISBN: 978-0-9886653-7-8
www.Crafterina.com

The *Sleeping Beauty* Story

Sleeping Beauty is one of the world's most famous ballets. Performed in four parts, the original choreography was created by Marius Petipa with music composed by Pyotr Ilyich Tchaikovsky.

Prologue

The story begins with a party for baby Princess Aurora. Guests welcome the newborn with dances and six magical fairies present her with gifts. Soon the celebration is interrupted by Carabosse, an evil fairy. Upset she was not invited, she decides to cast a spell that would cause the Princess to fall into a deep sleep on her sixteenth birthday. The Lilac Fairy reassures the King and Queen to not worry and vows to keep Princess Aurora safe.

ACT I

The story continues with Princess Aurora's 16th birthday at the castle. Carabosse arrives disguised in a large hooded cloak and gives a cursed bouquet of roses to the Princess. Delighted by the gesture, Aurora accepts them and accidentally pricks her finger on a thorn causing herself to fall into a deep sleep.

ACT II

The curtains open with Prince Désiré walking in the forest. He sees a vision of the Princess and dreams of meeting her one day. Keeping her promise and knowing he would break the spell, the Lilac Fairy leads the Prince to the castle. His love awakens the Princess and the spell is broken!

ACT III

The ballet finishes with a beautiful wedding and a happy ending for all!

Sleeping Beauty

The King and Queen with Princess Aurora

Sleeping Beauty

The Fairies
present
their gifts

Sleeping Beauty

Gifts for Princess Aurora

The Fairy of Tenderness gave the Princess a kind heart.

The Fairy of Generosity gave her a giving spirit.

The Fairy of Serenity gave the gift of calmness.

Sleeping Beauty

Gifts for Princess Aurora

The Fairy of Playfulness gave her fun spirited energy.

The Fairy of Courage gave the Princess strength of mind and spirit.

The Queen of the Fairies, the Lilac Fairy, gave the gift of love and protection.

Sleeping Beauty

The Fairy of Tenderness

Sleeping Beauty

The Fairy of Generosity

Sleeping Beauty

The Fairy of Serenity

Sleeping
Beauty

The Fairy of Playfulness

Sleeping Beauty

The Fairy of Courage

Sleeping Beauty

The Lilac Fairy

The Evil Fairy Carabosse

Sleeping Beauty

The Story Continues...

Princess Aurora celebrates her 16th birthday at the castle and performs a special dance called the Rose Adagio.

Carabosse casts an evil spell!

The Princess falls into a deep sleep. The Lilac Fairy vows to keep her safe and promises to help break the spell!

Sleeping Beauty

Princess Aurora and Prince Désiré

True love breaks the spell!

The Royal
Wedding

The White Cat and
Puss in Boots

The Royal
Wedding

The Wolf and
Red Riding Hood

Sleeping Beauty

The Royal Wedding

Sleeping Beauty

Let's create crafts!

Safety Note For Parents: These crafts require parent supervision to create.
There are pieces to cut out and will require your help. Have fun creating together!

Paper Dolls

Castle Dollhouse

Tiara

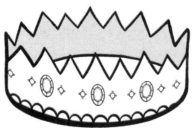

Crown

Rose Garland

Sleeping Beauty

Tiara Paper Craft

Directions:

1. — Cut out tiara template

2. Connect ends with glue or tape to make ring

3.  Time to celebrate!

Sleeping Beauty

Crown Paper Craft

Directions:

1. —Cut out crown template
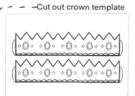

2. Connect ends with glue or tape to make ring
 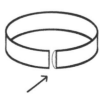

3. Time to celebrate!

www.Crafterina.com

Sleeping Beauty

Rose Garland Paper Craft

Directions:

1. Cut out garland strips

2. Connect ends with glue or tape to make ring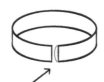

3. Continue adding rings to make garland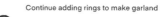

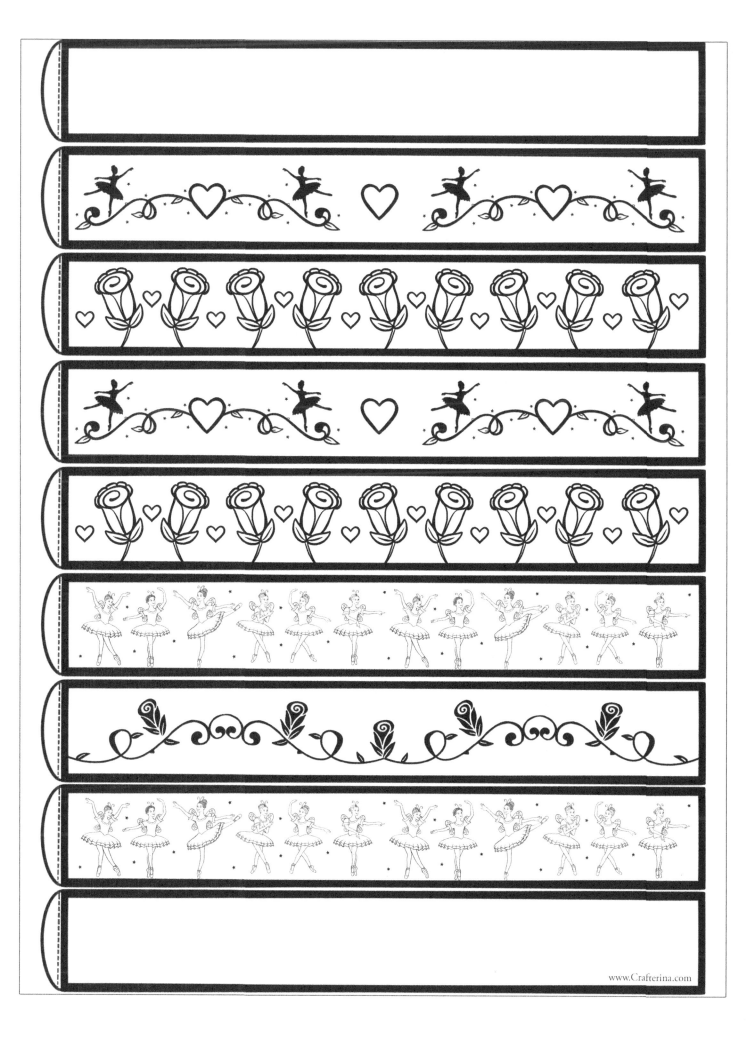

Sleeping Beauty

Castle Dollhouse Craft Directions

1. Color and cut out castle template

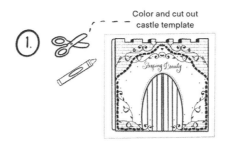

2. Cut along front door dotted line. Fold doors outward to open.

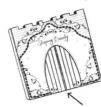

3. Use glue or tape on side tabs to connect walls together to make 3D castle

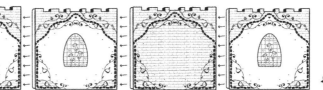

4. Cut out characters and fold in half along center dotted line and use tape or glue to secure.

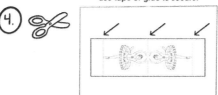

Fold bottom tabs outwards to make stand up.

5. Bravo! You're finished!

Sleeping Beauty

Front of Castle

Sleeping Beauty

Inside Front of Castle

Sleeping Beauty

Castle Side Panel

Inside Side Panel of Castle

Sleeping Beauty

Castle Side Panel

Inside Side Panel of Castle

Sleeping Beauty

Back of Castle

Sleeping Beauty

Castle Puppets

Princess Aurora

Prince Désiré

The Queen

The King

The Fairy of Generosity

The Fairy of Playfulness

The Evil Fairy Carabosse

The Fairy of Serenity

The Fairy of Tenderness

The Fairy of Playfulness

The Lilac Fairy

Sleeping Beauty

Princess Aurora Paper Doll Craft

Sleeping Beauty

Prince Désiré Paper Doll Craft

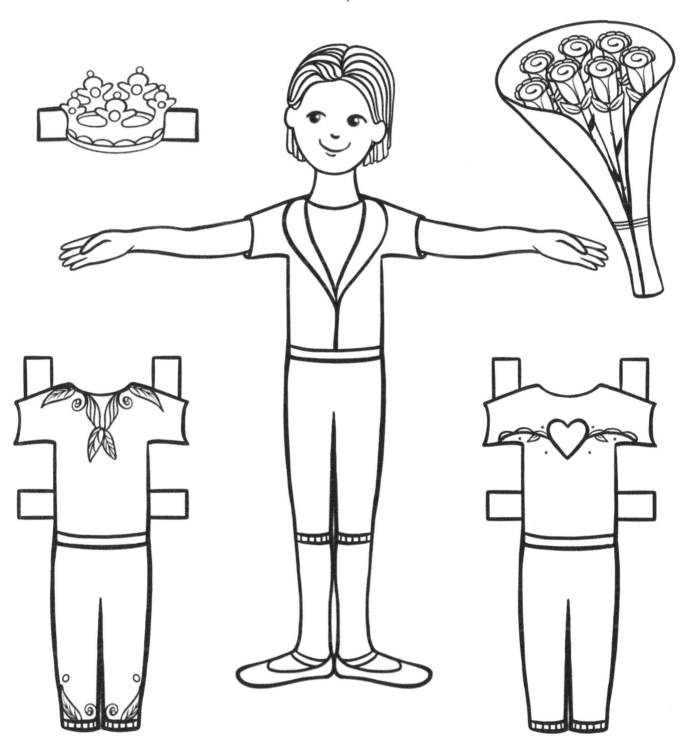

About the Author

Vanessa Salgado is a Professional Dancer, Educator and Illustrator.

She has taught many little dancers across Manhattan, concentrating primarily at the Joffrey Ballet School, School at STEPS on Broadway, and Alvin Ailey School. She has also worked as an Associate for the Education Department at New York City Center. Vanessa is a graduate of the Alvin Ailey/Fordham University BFA Program at Lincoln Center and holds a certification in Dance Education. Her work has been featured in Dance Teacher Magazine, Dance Spirit, Dance Informa, and METRO US Newspaper, among others.

Her earliest memories involve story time with her dad, creating with her mom after school, and attending weekend ballet class alongside her sister, Donna. Her interests in visual art blossomed in high school as she simultaneously trained for the professional dance world. As she transitioned from her college days into professional life, her incessant doodles and crafting have remained a source of wonder for all those around her.

For more information:
www.VanessaSalgado.com

About Crafterina®

Vanessa is also the creator of Crafterina® a series of dance education books and crafts for families. Designed to spark imagination and inspire movement at home, Crafterina® uniquely incorporates reading, creating and dancing in one. Through this interdisciplinary approach, Crafterina® playfully encourages empowerment and teaches youngsters they have the ability to make anything possible.

Inspire a lifelong love for learning in dance with the help of Crafterina®.

For more information, visit our website for books, crafts, and printables:

www.Crafterina.com

Crafterina

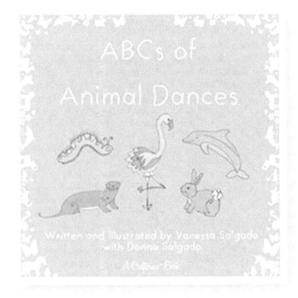

Find more from Crafterina by visiting:
www.Crafterina.com

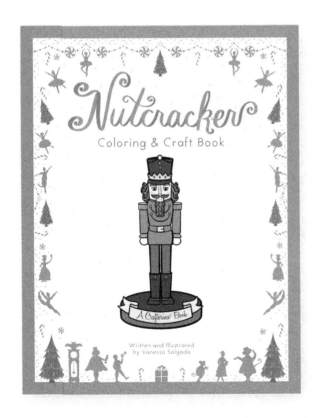

Made in the USA
Middletown, DE
18 October 2022